THE PAINTED
GARDEN

ISBN 0-7624-0482-5

Illustrations by Mary Woodin
Cover and interior designed by Rosemary Tottoroto

This book may be ordered by mail from the publisher.
Please include $2.50 for postage and handling.
BUT TRY YOUR BOOKSTORE FIRST!

Running Press Book Publishers
125 South Twenty-second Street
Philadelphia, Pennsylvania 19103-4399

Visit us on the web!
www.runningpress.com

THE PAINTED
GARDEN

A JOURNAL
WATERCOLOURS BY
MARY WOODIN

RUNNING PRESS
Philadelphia · London

If you would be happy for a week, take a wife,
If you would be happy for a month, kill your pig,
But if you would be happy all your life — plant a garden.

Chinese proverb

Riding on the crest of a wave that tries to submerge us is one of the phases of our existence that makes life most satisfactory and worth living, and it is the secret of all progress. If gardening were easy, even under favourable circumstances, we should none of us care to do it.

Mrs. C.W. Earle (1836-1925)
English writer

The fragile first petals
on the prunus

Iris Reticulata

anemone blanda
in the woodland
garden.

periwinkle - sorcerer's violet

Bees come out of their hives,
The partridge begins to pair,
The blackbird whistles,
and the field and woodlarks sing.

J.C. London (1783-1843)
Scottish horticultural writer

Half the interest of a garden is the constant exercise
of the imagination. You are always living three or
indeed six months hence. I believe that people entirely
devoid of imagination never can be really good gardeners.
To be content with the present, and not striving about
the future is fatal.

Mrs. C.W. Earle (1836-1925)
English Writer.

Fragaria
PINK PANDA

Ideal for border, hanging
baskets and containers

TOMATO
GARDENERS
DELIGHT

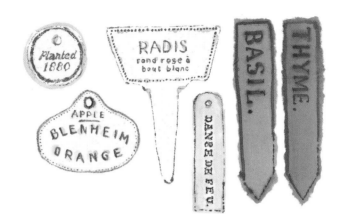

The love of gardening is a seed
that once sown never dies.

Gertrude Jekyll (1843-1932)
English landscape architect

These butterflies in twos and threes,
That flit about in wind and sun –
See how they add their flowers to flowers,
And blossom where a plant has none.

W.H. Davies (1871 – 1940)
Welsh poet

Here remember, that you never take in hand or begin the weeding of your beds, before the earth be made soft, through the store of rain, falling a day or two before.

Thomas Hyll
16th-century English writer

Is any moment of the year more delightful than the present? What there is wanting in glow of colour is more than made up for in fullness of interest. Each day some well-known long remembered plant bursts into blossom.

Henry A. Bright (1830 - 1884)
English horticultural writer

To create a little flower
is the labour of ages.

William Blake (1757-1827)
English poet.

Most operations may be performed
with common gloves. Thus, no gardener
need have hands like bear's paws.

J.C. Loudon (1783-1843)
Scottish horticultural writer.

I have recently heard it advocated as a short cut to harmony that all red and scarlet flowers be banished from the garden. This, I think, would be sad indeed, for much of warmth and strength, of flash and spirit would depart with them.

Louise Beebe Wilder (1878-1938)
American writer

The beauty there is in mosses
will have to be considered from
the holiest quietest nook.

Henry David Thoreau (1817 -1862)
American writer

This little space which scented box encloses
Is blue with lupins and is sweet with thyme
My garden all is overblown with roses,
My spirit is all overblown with rhyme,
As like a drunken honeybee I waver
From house to garden and again to house,
And undetermined which delight to favour,
On verse and rose alternately carouse.

Vita Sackville-West (1892-1962)
English writer

There should be beds of roses, banks of roses, bowers of roses, hedges of roses, edgings of roses, baskets of roses, vistas and alleys of roses.

Rev. Samuel Reynolds Hole
A Book about Roses, 1869

A bank whereon the wild thyme blows
Where oxlips and the nodding violet grows
Quite over-canopied with luscious woodbine
With sweet musk roses and with eglantine.

William Shakespeare (1564 - 1616)
English playwright

Blue! Gentle cousin of the forest green,
Married to green in all the sweetest flowers.

John Keats (1795 - 1821)
English poet

Rose, rose and clematis,
Trail and twine and
clasp and kiss.

Alfred Lord Tennyson (1809 - 1892)
English poet

I wish I could paint the hues of these splendid
delphiniums, such shades of melting blue, some
light, others dark, some like the summer heaven,
and dashed across their pale azure wings
with delicious rose.

Celia Thaxter (1835-1894)
American poet

I know nothing so pleasant as to sit there on a summer afternoon, with the western sun flickering through the great elder-tree, and lighting up our gay parterres, where flowers and flowering shrubs are set as thick as grass in a field, a wilderness of blossom, interwoven, intertwined, wreathy, garlandy, profuse beyond all profusion.

Mary Mitford (1787-1855)
English horticultural writer

The poetry of the earth is never dead.
John Keats (1795-1821)
English poet.

For those who have not got very good memories for the names of plants, I strongly recommend them if they can draw to make a little coloured sketch, however small on the page of a gardening book next the name of the plant. This will be found a great help to the memory.

Mrs. C. W. Earle (1836 - 1925)
English writer

The sun has shone on the earth,
and the golden rod is his fruit.

Henry David Thoreau (1817-1862)
American writer

FLOWER SEEDS.

PANSY
GIANT
MIXED

AVERAGE
CONTENTS
100 SEEDS

There are few things to be done in a garden which do not require a dexterity in operation and a nicety in hitting the proper season for doing it.

J. C. London (1783 - 1843)
Scottish horticultural writer

Under the influence of all this loveliness,
almost I am persuaded to love autumn best,
and forget a lifelong allegiance to the
spring-time of the year. Such infidelity
could be brought about by nothing less
than a month like this, so wondrously,
serenely beautiful.

E. V. Boyle (1825 - 1916)
Sylvana's Letter to an Unknown Friend

It is a very good plan, when you want to cut a new bed or alter the shape of an old one, to shuffle along the wet dewy grass on an October morning – and this leaves a mark which enables you very well to judge the size, shape, and proportion before you begin to cut your beds out.

Mrs. C. W. Earle (1836 - 1925)
English writer.

The garden is never dead ;
growth is always going on
and growth that can be seen,
and seen with delight.

Canon H. Ellacombe
<u>In My Vicarage Garden and Elsewhere</u>, 1901

Everything is good in its season.
Italian proverb

Even deep snow gives time for cleaning,
thrashing and sorting of seeds,
preparing stakes and pea-sticks,
tying mats, sorting bulbs.

J. C. Loudon (1783-1843)
Scottish horticultural writer

Gardens are not made by sitting in the shade.
Rudyard Kipling (1865 - 1936)
English writer